CLARINET PREP TEST

Dear clarinet player

Congratulations! You have reached a stage when you can play to an examiner and achieve your first certificate. The skills you will use include a sense of pitch and rhythm, accuracy and making a pleasant and even sound or 'tone'. You will be with the examiner for about 10 minutes, during which time you will play the tunes, pieces and answer the listening games. You may have your own accompanist for the pieces or the examiner can accompany you. The examiner's comments and suggestions will be written on the certificate given to you at the end of the test. You might like to have it framed, so that it will always be a reminder of this special occasion.

I hope you enjoy the tunes, pieces and listening games in this book, as well as the illustrations and Fun Page. This is the first step on what will be an exciting and lifelong musical journey.

Now on to the music!

Clara Taylor
Chief Examiner

1 Tunes

The examiner will want to hear you play all three of these tunes. You will have to play them from memory, so once you have learnt them remember to keep your book closed when you are practising!

a) Steady Eddie

Play this piece with an even pulse and clear tonguing.
Make sure to give the long notes their full value.

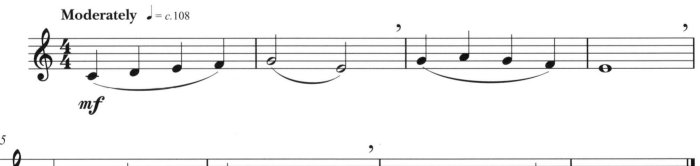

CLARINET Prep Test

This book belongs to:

....

Date of Prep Test:

....

Examiner's signature:

....

The Associated Board of the Royal Schools of Music

b) Leapin' Lucy

Beware: this piece contains large leaps! Always use a firm finger action and breathe where marked.

c) Bouncin' Ben

Use lots of air in order to make your tongue really 'bounce' on the repeated notes. Always count carefully in ¾ as the first beat of the next bar comes sooner than you think!

2 Set Piece

Your set piece can be any one of the five pieces printed on pages 6, 7, 8 and 9 – 'Funky Monkey', 'Countryside Waltz', 'Bus Stop Blues', 'Mission to Mars' or 'The French Detective'. Alternatively, you may choose any piece from *Party Time!* for Clarinet (published by ABRSM Publishing). If you select 'Mission to Mars', 'The French Detective' or a piece from *Party Time!*, either your accompanist or the examiner will play it with you. Your teacher will help you to choose the right piece.

Funky Monkey

James Rae

Countryside Waltz

James Rae

Bus Stop Blues

James Rae

Mission to Mars

James Rae

The French Detective

James Rae

Bright jazz waltz ♩ = *c*.130

mp espress.

mf *mp*

f *mp*

p

3 Own Choice Piece

We would like you to play this with either your accompanist or the examiner, so you need to choose a piece with a piano accompaniment. As we want you to play something you really enjoy, we have left the choice up to you. If you like, you can play one of the accompanied set pieces from this book, as long as it is different from you first piece! Whichever piece you choose, remember to bring the piano part for whoever is accompanying you.

4 Listening Games

In these games the examiner will be playing pieces of music like the examples printed below.

Game A: Clapping the beat

In this first game, the examiner will play a short piece in 2 or 3 time. You should join in as soon as possible by clapping or tapping the beat.

   All music has a beat, so you can practise this game at home with your friends whenever you are listening to music on the radio or a recording.

Game B: Echoes

In this game, the examiner will clap two simple two-bar rhythms in 2 or 3 time. After each one, you should clap the rhythm back to the examiner in time and as an echo. The examiner will count in two bars before the first rhythm.

   Practise this game at home with a friend or parent. Did you clap *exactly* the same rhythm? Did you clap it back in rhythm or was there a pause?

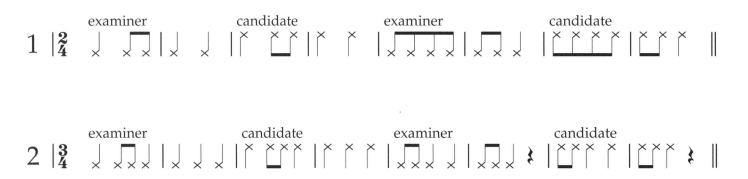

Game C: Finding the notes

Now the examiner will play a group of three notes to you, two times through. The game is to sing these notes back to the examiner after the second playing. They will be played in 'free time', so you don't need to worry about the rhythm. If you don't want to sing, you can play the notes on your clarinet, in which case the examiner will play a group using only C, D and E – you have to find all three notes, including the starting note! Here are some examples:

Game D: What can you hear?

In this last game, listen as the examiner plays another short piece of music. The examiner will want to know whether the piece was played loudly or quietly (the 'dynamic' of the piece), or whether it was fast or slow (the 'tempo' of the piece). The examiner will choose one of these and tell you which one to listen out for before he or she plays.

   Practise this game at home with your friends whenever you are playing or listening to a piece of music.

i) *Is this piece loud or quiet?*

ii) *Is this piece fast or slow?*

Fun Page

Music is written down on five lines known as a 'stave'. A few empty staves are printed below: you can use these to practise drawing notes, rests, clefs and time signatures (if you don't understand any of these words, ask your teacher or look in *First Steps in Music Theory*, published by ABRSM Publishing). Or you can write down some tunes of your own.

Word Search

This word search contains 12 musical words, listed below. How many can you find? Do you know what they all mean?

C	L	A	R	I	N	E	T	C	I
B	L	J	S	F	D	Y	H	E	T
O	M	E	C	L	E	G	A	T	O
I	H	B	F	T	R	U	V	T	N
P	T	I	O	C	K	H	A	P	E
D	Y	N	A	M	I	C	B	Q	F
S	H	K	Y	E	C	S	Z	G	D
L	R	W	D	A	S	T	A	V	E
M	O	U	T	H	P	I	E	C	E
A	B	S	O	S	L	U	R	J	R

Words to find:
clarinet
reed
mouthpiece
clef
staccato
stave
legato
dynamic
slur
rhythm
note
tone

We hope you enjoyed doing the Prep Test and look forward to seeing you at Grade 1!

05.08 Printed in England by Halstan & Co. Ltd, Amersham, Bucks

The French Detective

James Rae

Clarinet Prep Test

Piano Accompaniments

Mission to Mars

James Rae

AB 3419